DISNEY XD™

EGMONT
We bring stories to life

First published in Great Britain in 2011 by Egmont UK Limited
239 Kensington High Street, London W8 6SA
All rights reserved.

Editor: Catherine Such • Writer: Olivia McLearon
• Designer: Rod Edwards • Editorial Assistant: Hannah Greenfield
• Group Art Editor: Jeanette Ryall • Group Editor: Keilly Swift

ISBN 978 1 4052 5688 9
1 3 5 7 9 10 8 6 4 2
Printed in Italy

Photographs: p.23 © Getty; p.24 main image, bottom right
© Getty; p.25 top left © PA photos, top right and bottom left
© Getty, middle left © Robert Brown/BillabongXXLcom; p.42
© PA Photos; p. 43 top left and centre © Rex, top right
and bottom right © Getty; p. 51 © Getty; p. 52 bottom
left © Getty; p.52–53 centre © Getty; p.53 centre right
© Alamy, bottom right © Rex.

Phineas and Ferb: Based on the series created by Dan Povenmire and Jeff "Swampy" Marsh.

This annual belongs to

Name ~~[name scribbled out]~~

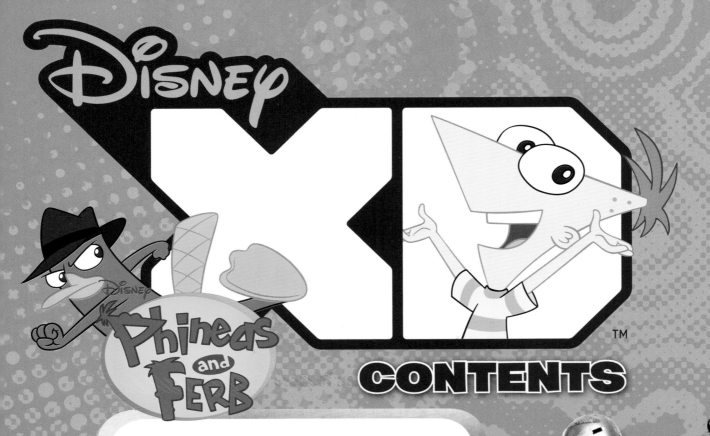

DISNEY XD

CONTENTS

Phineas and Ferb

Disney ZEKE AND LUTHER

Meet the Gang

Discover everything you need to know about Phineas and Ferb and the brilliantly bonkers world they live in.

BEST FRIENDS AND BROTHERS

Excitable and super-smart **Phineas** (right) and strong but silent **Ferb** (left) are best friends and stepbrothers. They spend their holidays making massive awesome inventions and doing the most amazing activities. Phineas has lots of big ideas and Ferb helps bring those inventions to life!

PHINEAS AND FERB FACTS

The boys once carved their sister Candace's head onto Mount Rushmore for her birthday!

The brothers have made some wicked inventions, including a rollercoaster and a rocket!

THE REST OF THE CLAN

Candace is Phineas' older sister and Ferb's stepsister. She's forever trying to land her brothers in trouble by telling her mom what they've been up to. But their inventions nearly always disappear before their mom sees them! Her other main obsession in life is **Jeremy**. He starts out as a crush, but then becomes her boyfriend.

Linda Flynn-Fletcher is Phineas and Candace's mother and Ferb's stepmother. She used to be a famous pop star! She's married to **Lawrence** – Ferb's dad – an archaeologist who never quite realises what's going on under his nose.

CANDACE

They've got a pet platypus called Perry, who's got a mysterious secret ...

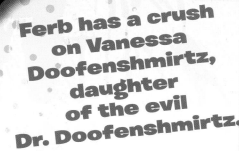

Ferb has a crush on Vanessa Doofenshmirtz, daughter of the evil Dr. Doofenshmirtz.

D vs P

Perry the Platypus is the Flynn-Fletchers' pet platypus. But he's not just any old platypus – he lives a secret double life as **Agent P**, a crime-fighting member of the all-animal spy organisation, the O.W.C.A. (Organisation Without a Cool Acronym).

Dr. Doofenshmirtz has one big ambition in life – to take over the entire tri-state area that Phineas, Ferb and their family and friends live in! He attempts to do this with different crazy inventions, but Agent P always manages to put a stop to his plans!

DID YOU KNOW?

So how do Phineas and Ferb's inventions mysteriously disappear at the end of the day? That's mostly the work of Agent P! Not that Phineas, Ferb or Candace realise!

THE PHINEAS AND FERB CREW

Buford, **Baljeet** and **Isabella** are all good friends with Phineas and Ferb. Isabella is the leader of the **Fireside Girls** troop and has a huge crush on Phineas! Buford may seem scary, but he's mainly a good friend to the gang and Baljeet is Phineas and Ferb's neighbour. He's super-brainy and very polite.

Jeremy is Candace's crush, later boyfriend. He's relaxed, laid back and the lead singer and guitarist for his band **Jeremy and the Incidentals**. The other mega important person in Candace's life is **Stacy**, her confident and enthusiastic best friend.

ISABELLA

JEREMY

BALJEET

BUFORD

Plot: Michael Stewart   Script: Dan Povenmire and Jeff "Swampy" Marsh   Pencils & Inks: Min S. Ku   Colors: John Green   Letters: Michael Stewart   Based on the series created by Dan Povenmire & Jeff "Swampy" Marsh . © Disney Enterprises Inc.

"STUFF LIKE FIGHTING A MUMMY...

"...OR CLIMBING UP THE *EIFFEL TOWER*...

"...OR SURFING TIDAL WAVES, OR--"

HEY, WHERE'S PERRY?

REMEMBER, THE *FAMILY* YOU LIVE WITH MUST *NEVER* SUSPECT THAT YOU ARE WORKING FOR THE GOVERNMENT!

WELL, FERB-- WHAT ARE WE GOING TO DO *TOMORROW*?

THE BEGINNING!

Disney Phineas and Ferb

Puzzling Puzzles

Can you help Phineas and Ferb with these fun brain-teasers?

SCRAMBLED!

Unscramble the letters to work out what Dr. Doofenshmirtz is saying.

"Sjut tutpnig eht nsihingif hosutec no ym etastl viel panl."

Write the unscrambled sentence here. Some letters have been filled in for you:

Just putting the finishing touches on my latest evil plan.

THE MISSING WORD

What word is missing from this funny Ferb quote?

"It was definitely better than the .... in the cake."

★ Train ★ Gorilla ✓
★ Strawberry jam ★ Tree

ODD PHINEAS OUT

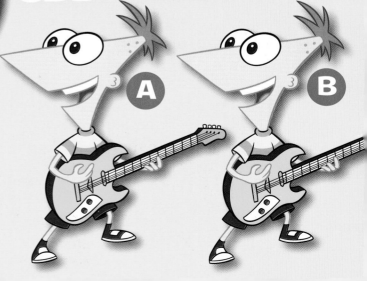

A   B

JIGSAW JUMBLE

Can you work out which two pieces are missing from the picture of Agent P?

ANSWERS ON PAGE 68

Which of these five pics is the odd one out?

15

Writer: Scott Peterson   Pencils: John Green   Inks: Mike DeCarlo   Colors: Emily Kanalz   Letters: Michael Stewart   Based on the series created by Dan Povenmire & Jeff "Swampy" Marsh © 2011 Disney Enterprises, Inc.

Top Secret Wordsearch

Can you find these 12 characters in the wordsearch?

They read forwards, backwards, horizontal, vertically and diagonally.

```
L M Z C W I W E G A W B I C J M W B O H
Z M Z A R G O N O M R O J A M T H Y D B L Y
K U Q R F N E L X V P Y B R L D M H Z B F L L
Z F L G N Y K H N Z R C T I Z O S O D G Z Z Q
N I L Z F X E H E A R P O I M L F I I F X C Q
Q O F C G X N R D P X G H Z C E D A J H X B B
O K N X G Y R T N P T A C Y F E X H D Z A X P
L K B D D R E P T X E P A V D F M C G M L
W V V G N T N E B E L O T A H L H B V X
T Q S A I B E L W U F E I L J Q Z H E N H
P M V I D D R O F U B S E N I Q G A R
I P T Q Z E S E H A Y K F Q G R R E
U F D E Z R O Y S K B M Q H R T H
T U P G W O H A B M Y H F N T S
V P E Y N H X N M G R L G Z
L P W Y J M R X I R V D G
U K B J R O
```

ANSWERS ON PAGE 68

PHINEAS · CANDACE · AGENT P · BUFORD

FERB · DOOFENSHMIRTZ · JEREMY

ISABELLA · BALJEET · GRETCHEN

LINDA · MAJOR MONOGRAM

17

Writer: Jim Bernstein Pencils: John Green Inks: Mike DeCarlo Colors: Garry Black Letters: Michael Stewart Based on the series created by Dan Povenmire & Jeff "Swampy" Marsh © 2011 Disney Enterprises, Inc.

"DINO-MIGHT!"

YOU KNOW, FERB, MAYBE IT WASN'T SUCH A GOOD IDEA TO MAKE OUR OWN DINOSAUR.

YA THINK?

EARLIER THAT DAY...

DINO-WORLD

THESE FAKE DINOSAURS DON'T LOOK SCARY AT ALL.

I DO NOT AGREE.

I HAVE HAD TO CHANGE MY UNDERPANTS THREE TIMES SINCE WE ARRIVED.

THIS FAKE DINOSAUR GIVES ME AN IDEA!

FERB, I KNOW WHAT WE'RE GONNA DO TODAY!

DOES IT INVOLVE CLONING A DINOSAUR?

WHY, YES. YES, IT DOES.

PHINEAS... AND... FERB... I... AM... SO... MAD... AT... YOU!

FLUFFY SEEMED TO BE ATTRACTED TO THE BRIGHT RED COLOR OF THE SQUEAKY TOY.

MAYBE WE CAN LURE HIM AWAY FROM CANDACE WITH SOMETHING ELSE THAT'S RED.

I HOPE CANDACE WILL BE OKAY UNTIL WE CATCH UP WITH HER!

OH, SHE'S PRETTY GOOD AT TAKING CARE OF HERSELF.

WELL, PERRY THE PLATYPUS, THIS TIME YOU'RE TOO LATE!

MY STICKY-INATOR WILL MAKE EVERYTHING IN THE TRI-STATE AREA UNBEARABLY STICKY.

I DON'T KNOW WHY I PAINTED IT RED. JUST TRYING TO MIX THINGS UP A LITTLE.

AHHH-HHHH-HHHH-HHHH!

CHOMP!

RECORD BREAKERS:

WATER

Oh my! These wild water record breakers totally rule!

1 Longest surfing session Bill Laity surfed for 26 hours, riding 147 waves. Simply incredible!

2 Youngest and oldest winner of ASP championships Kelly Slater won this surfing title at 20 and 38! (Plus another eight times.)

3 Longest swim Martin Strel swam the entire length of the Amazon River in 2007 – that's 5268km!

4 Most people to water ski at one time 114 Australian water skiers broke this record in 2010. They were towed by a huge catamaran!

5 Longest time holding breath under water Karoline Mariechen Meyer held her breath for 18 minutes, 32 seconds – **crazy!**

6 Youngest ever medalist in a world diving event Tom Daley took part in the 2007 Australian Youth Olympics at 12 – you normally have to be 15!

7 Deepest free dive using no apparatus Carlos Coste swam 150m through a cave, with no breathing apparatus – amazing!

8 Quickest woman to swim the 800m Brit Rebecca Adlington smashed this record in eight minutes 14.10 seconds at the 2008 olympics!

9 Youngest person to sail around the world 16 year old Australian, Jessica Watson, spent seven months sailing around the world!

10 Longest distance surfing Serginho Laus rode for 33 mins and 15 seconds, covering 10.1km. Wowzers!

RIDE THE WAVES

Whether you're keen to hop on a board and splash it out, or a seasoned surf pro - be inspired by some of the best surfer kids in the biz ...

Surfing first started in Hawaii in the 19th century and spread to the Californian coast in the 1920s.

MILES LEE HARGREAVES

Surf kid champ, Miles Lee Hargreaves, from the under 16s British Junior Surf Team, started learning to ride the waves when he was just a tiny tot. Miles' big love of chasing waves developed into a serious hobby at the age of 6 and by 10 he was entering in competitions. He's since travelled all over the world to train and won tons of cool awards. In 2010 Miles' competed as part of the British Junior Surf Team at the ISA World Championships in Piha, New Zealand. He said, "I'm really proud. It's a once in a lifetime opportunity and it gives you a chance to potentially win a world title." **Totally rad!**

47 surfers rode the world's largest surfboard (40ft long), at Snapper Rocks on March 5, 2005, in Australia.

TASSY SWALLOW

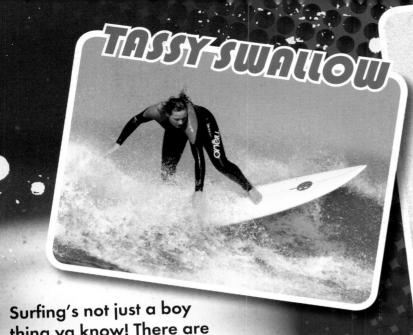

Surfing's not just a boy thing ya know! There are loads of cool surfer chicks, like under 16s pro, Tassy Swallow, proving that girls have caught the surf bug, too. Tassy says, "I want to get to the top in Europe and and take girl's surfing to the world!"

The biggest wave ever ridden by a surfer was Mike Parsons' 75-footer at the Cortes Bank, California in 2008.

PATRICK DANIEL

Miles and Tassy's squad mate, Patrick, loves getting barrelled by the ocean. "You are completely covered up by the ocean and you can look through the barrel and see the daylight." A surf barrel is when a wave wraps around you, so that you're inside a barrel-like wave, kinda like a tube.

TOP TIPS

Suit up!
The water'll be cold, so always wear a wetsuit to keep warm and protect your skin.

Board is best
Beginners should start out with a long board. Long boards are between 8–10 feet long and are easier to paddle and catch waves with when you're new to surfing.

Lesson learnt
Surfing can be dangerous, so take at least a couple of lessons before you start. Find a qualified instructor with 5–10 years experience.

Fitness freak!
Get as fit as you can. You'll need good upper body strength and to be flexible too, so do lots of stretching.

Balance Out
Try using a balance board at home to practise your technique.

Introducing

Disney ZEKE AND LUTHER

Want to find out more about Zeke and Luther? Then read on!

ALL ABOUT ZEKE

Zeke is 16 years old and totally mad about skateboarding. He's best friends with Luther. He's got a way too smart younger sister called Ginger, as well as a major crush on the girl next door, Olivia Masterson.

SMART ALEC GINGER

Ginger is Zeke's clever younger sister. She's got great business sense – she used Zeke and Luther to try and make money in "Bros Go Pro"! One of her main pleasures in life is annoying her older brother in as many ways as she can.

ROCKIN' LUTHER

Luther's been skateboarding with his best friend Zeke for 10 years. One of their top moments was meeting their idol, pro-skateboarder Tony Hawk!

GO GO KOJO!

Kojo's a kind of frenemy to Zeke and Luther! They're friends, but also big skateboarding rivals. He thinks that he's a better skater than the pair of them and will stop at nothing to beat them!

DID YOU KNOW?

Luther once had to choose between saving his knee and saving Zeke!

Ginger once planned her own surprise birthday party. (How does that work?!)

Kojo has his own calendar!

Luther's surname is Waffles!

Zeke's real name is Ezekiel!

Zeke and Luther once fought over who got to keep a pair of Tony Hawk's boxer shorts!

Puzzling with

DISNEY ZEKE AND LUTHER

Can you help the super skaters with all of these puzzles?

GET YOUR SKATES ON!

Help Zeke, Luther and Kojo race their way through the maze, avoiding Ginger on the way.

START

FINISH

TOTAL CHANGES

Can you work out the five crazy changes in picture two?

1

2

ANSWERS ON PAGE 68

WHO IS IT?

Look at these three facts. Which character is being described?

1 She's really smart.

2 She likes making money.

3 She's Zeke's younger sister.

An interview with
DISNEY
ZEKE AND LUTHER

We caught up with Hutch Dano and Adam Hicks, who play Zeke and Luther, and got the low-down from behind the scenes on the show.

HUTCH DANO **ZEKE**

You and Adam play best friends in Zeke and Luther. Are you friends off-set too?

We are – we have great chemistry on screen and started our friendship when we did the audition.

What's the best thing about working together?

It's always a great experience when you love doing a show but when your co-star happens to be a good friend, it makes it even better.

What's on your iPod right now?

Eminem and Led Zeppelin.

What's different about Season Three?

Everyone really evolved in season three – the writing, the characters. It's better than ever before!

Are there any new characters?

There are great new guest stars on the show this season. This is what helps make the show great – we are adding even more fantastic talent to the ensemble.

What funny stuff happened on set during Season Three?

We pull pranks on each other on set all the time. Whether it is slapping stuff out of each other's hands to distract us or freaking people out behind doors, there is always goofy stuff going on around the set.

What do you think readers will find most surprising about Season Three?

They will get to see how many times Zeke and Luther's friendship gets really tested.

Can you give us some tips for being good at skateboarding?

My top tips are:
• Always wear safety pads.
• Make sure you look around.
• Don't skate too fast.
• Practise a trick before trying it for real.

ADAM HICKS
LUTHER

You and Hutch play best friends in Zeke and Luther. Are you friends off-set too?

We are lucky in the fact that on our show we are like one big happy family and we all look out for each other. We have great chemistry on set and we all try to keep in touch when we are off set.

What's the best thing about working together?

Hutch and I can look at each other and know what each other are thinking, which really helps us work well on screen too.

What's on your iPod right now?

My iPod has a mixture of music. I love writing my own rap music and so I listen to a lot of that genre – Drake and Jay Z. I also admire Taylor Swift and I like Celine Dion and David Bowie.

What's different about the third season?

Season three is full of great surprises and lots of action that I know our fans will enjoy. We have such great writers and it's an honour to be able to work the comedy they write for me.

Are there any new characters?

I have to keep it quiet ... can't give all our secrets away. I would just say be sure to tune in!

What do you think readers will find most surprising about Season Three?

I think they will just relate even more with the characters now that they have had time to see them develop.

What surprising stuff did you learn about your co-stars?

Well, we have all kind of grown up with each other and developed our characters. We get to work with a really awesome group of very talented writers, producers, directors and crew that have become like a second family.

Can you give us some tips for being good at skateboarding?

I have been able to meet the greats of the skateboarding world and they have passed on to me that it takes dedication and hard work to reach your goals, but if it's your dream then you can do it!

Disney
ZEKE AND LUTHER
puzzle time

How quickly can you solve these awesome skater puzzles?

1 SKATER PILE UP

How many times can you spot each of these cool stickers in this pile up?

2

PICTURE PUZZLER

Which close-up isn't taken from this image of Zeke and Luther?

SUPER SUDOKU

Can you put each character's initial in the right place on the grid to complete the puzzle?

K

3

The Rules

Z

Each character can only appear once in each row, column and box!

G

ANSWERS ON PAGE **68**

33

All About

Disney KICK BUTTOWSKI
suburban daredevil

Kick Buttowski is a pretty normal 12 year old boy. Except that he's also a Suburban Daredevil!

DAREDEVIL

Kick's got one ambition in life. He's determined to be a daredevil and he tries to make every day involve some danger! In fact, Kick (or Clarence as his parents named him!), lives every day as if it was his own personal action movie.

THE BEST FRIEND

Kick's best friend is Gunther, the son of two Vikings. He also acts as his stunt coordinator. Unlike Kick, he worries a lot and he doesn't have a sense of adventure.

LOOKING THE PART

Kick dresses the part in a white jumpsuit with red stripes down the sleeves, a white helmet with a red stripe and yellow boots and gloves. He even wears it to school!

BAD BRAD

Kick's annoying brother, Brad constantly calls him "dillweed". But Kick got his revenge when he mastered "Dead Man's Drop" and humiliated Brad in the process. Sweet revenge!

THE IDOLS

Billy Stumps is a very famous daredevil, and Kick's idol. But he's not the only tough guy who Kick's met. Papercut Peterson helped Kick defeat Brad, along with his brother Shogun Sanchez.

KICK'S CATCHPHRASE!

MEET THE FAMILY

As well as an annoying older brother, Kick's also got a bratty younger sister. Brianna is very spoilt and takes part in lots of beauty pageants.

Aw, biscuits!

Show time! ✓

This is gonna Kick Buttowski!

Chimichanga!

S I O T E H W M M

Unscramble the letters above to find out which catchphrase Kick is shouting?

ANSWERS ON PAGE 68

KICK IT!

Disney **KICK BUTTOWSKI** Suburban daredevil

Use the grid to help you draw Kick Buttowski.

BUTTOWSKI WORDSEARCH!

Find the 12 Kick Buttowski related words in the wordsearch!

They read forwards, backwards, horizontally, vertically and diagonally.

DAREDEVIL ✓
CLARENCE ✓
GUNTHER ✓
CHIMICHANGA ✓

DILLWEED ✓
BRIANNA ✓
WADE ✓
BILLY STUMPS ✓

KENDALL ✓
MR VICKLE ✓
PANTSIE ✓
KYLE ✓

ANSWERS ON PAGE 68

37

KICK BUTTOWSKI
suburban daredevil

FUNNIEST MOMENTS

Kick Buttowski is properly hilarious! Laugh your socks off at these funny moments.

HOW PANTS!

AND ANOTHER THING ... ERM, WHERE ARE YOUR CLOTHES, KICK?!

NOSE TO NOSE!

IF I STAND HERE LIKE THIS FOR LONG ENOUGH, WILL I REALLY, REALLY INTIMIDATE YOU?

AS IF, BLONDIE!

FLAT OUT

NOT THE MOST COMFORTABLE PLACE I'VE EVER LANDED ...

TRUE MY FRIEND!

SPLAT!

BANG ON THE BUS

BANG!

GREAT HAMSTER IMPRESSION, KICK, HA HA HA!

MOP POWER!

EVEN MOPS GET THE **DAREDEVIL TREATMENT** WHEN I'M AROUND!

KICK RULES!

SHOW TIME!

GET GIRLY

PINK FLOWERS ARE SO YOU, KICK!

ARGH!

COOL AS ICE

GUNTHER, DO YOUR THING!

SNOW BOARDING

CHECK ME OUT!

TRUE OR FALSE?

Can you tell the Kick Buttowski facts from the fiction? Find out with this test!

1 Gunther's parents own a restaurant called Battlesnax.

2 Wade works at the train station.

3 Kick's idol is Bobby Stumps.

5 Kick is really good friends with Kendall Perkins.

6 Papercut Peterson is a professional wrestler.

7 Shogun Sanchez is Papercut Peterson's younger brother.

4 Kick goes to Mellowbrook Elementary school.

8 Wacky Jackie's surname is Wackmann.

9 Kick's real name is Clarence Francis Buttowski.

10 Kick sometimes gets called Prawn.

11 Kick's dad's car is called Joelle.

12 Oskar the dog regularly destroys Kick's homework.

13 Pantsie has a little brother called Nose.

14 Kick and Brad won a trip to Hawaii in 'Things That Make You Go Boom'.

15 Ronaldo is obsessed by physics.

Answers!
1 True, **2** false – he works at a gas station, **3** false – it's Billy Stumps, **4** true, **5** false – they hate each other! **6** true, **7** false – he's his older brother, **8** false – it's Wackerman, **9** true, **10** false – he sometimes gets called Shrimp, **11** false – it's called Monique, **12** false – it's only happened once, **13** false – he's called Mouth, **14** true, **15** true.

HOW DID YOU DO?

1 - 6: We're setting up some kickin' homework!
Watch a couple of episodes of Kick Buttowski on Disney XD and then re-do the quiz - your score is bound to jump right up!

6 - 10: Not too bad. But there's definitely room for improvement.
Give yourself a kick-start by re-reading the Kick section and then taking the quiz again!

11 - 15: Wow, you're a total KB expert!
He lives his life as if he's a surburban daredevil and you live your life like a Kick Buttowski guru!

Daredevil STUNTS!

Check out some of the craziest stunts ever attempted - and the people who made them happen (or tried to)!

I AM A LUCKY, LUCKY PERSON!

THE ULTIMATE REV!

The prize for the most iconic daredevil of all time goes to motorcycle stunt jumper, **Robbie 'Evel' Knievel**. In the 1960s/70s, Evel was famed more for his failures than his successes! His televised stunts still rank as some of the most watched sporting events of all time, earned him loads of entries in the Guinness Book of World Records and turned him into a total legend. During his career he jumped over rows of cars, trucks, the fountain at Caesars Palace hotel in Las Vegas, mountain lions and even a tank full of live sharks, with varying degrees of success. He also suffered a total of 37 broken bones during his career. **Ouch!**

BLAST OFF!

Current world record holder, David Smith Jr, is blasting his way to fame as the **'human cannonball'**. With over 5000 cannonball performances around the world and the title of the highest-flying human cannonball – he flies 200 feet into the air – there's just no stopping this rocket man!

WARNING!
DON'T TRY ANY OF THESE STUNTS AT HOME!!!

ERM, ACTUALLY, CAN I GO BACK?

THE BIG DROP ...

Amazingly the first person to go over Niagara Falls in a barrel was actually 63 year old school teacher, **Annie Edson!** She specially designed the barrel herself and filled it with padding. Annie plunged over the 173ft horseshoe part of the falls in 1901, escaping with just a small gash on her head. That was one gutsy teach, eh?!

WALKING THE LINE

In 1974, Parisian street performer, Philippe Petit, famously **walked a tightrope** between the top floors of the Twin Tower buildings in New York City without official permission. He walked the wire for 45 minutes, making eight crossings, a quarter of a mile above the city, dancing, sitting and lying on the wire, too. He was arrested at the South Tower, but the charges were dropped in exchange for a free aerial show in Central Park for the kids of NYC!

WHO'S IN THE BAND?

Rock out with Iron Weasel! Meet the band, as well as Tripp's best friend ... and his mother!

WHAT BAND?

The band in question are the one and only ... **IRON WEASEL!** Originally made up of three 40-something rockers, 15 year old Tripp Campbell has the ultimate wish come true when he's invited to join his favourite band as lead guitarist – wowzers!

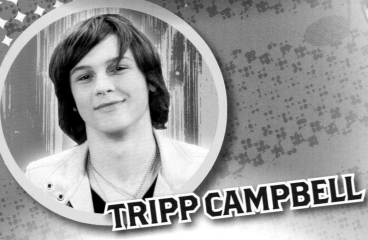

TRIPP CAMPBELL

Tripp is just a normal 15 year old boy, who also happens to be a member of a top rock band! After winning a competition to have dinner with Iron Weasel, he impresses them with his superior guitar-playing skills and ends up joining the band – despite any initial misgivings the rest of the band have!

DEREK JUPITER

Derek Jupiter's charming, charismatic and oozes confidence. So he makes the perfect lead singer for Iron Weasel! He sometimes worries that having Tripp in the band makes them a little less cool though.

BURGER PITT

Burger is the crazy bass player. He's been known to smash his bass to bits and even smash his head into a wall! He's got some really gross habits too!

ASH TAYLOR

The cool dude drummer of the band! He could never claim to be the most intelligent member of the band, but he's got a heart of gold and like the rest of the band, he loves to party!

ALSO...

Izzy is one of Tripp's best friends, who also happens to be a massive fan of Iron Weasel and Beth is Tripp's laid back and supportive mum who has to put up with Iron Weasel living in her house for a while!

IZZY FUENTES

BETH CAMPBELL

BRAIN

Can you work out the answers to these Iron Weasel puzzlers?

SPOT THE DIFFERENCE

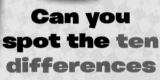

Can you spot the ten differences between these two pictures?

TEASERS

SHADOW ROCKER!

Can you work out which member of Iron Weasel has been shadowed out here?

A C M
C R B
M
W G
T C
U W
P A E
R
C T
A W M A

WORD PLAY

Cross out all of the letters that appear more than twice, then re-arrange the remaining letters to reveal a member of the band.

ANSWERS ON PAGE 68

BURGER PITT

47

The MEGA Band

Would you be the lead singer, a lead or bass guitarist or the drummer in your band? Find out with our quiz!

1 What role do you go for in the school play?

A You're far too cool for that kind of thing, but if you had to chose, it would be the lead of course.

B It would have to be a lead role – you've got the talent for it!

C A smaller role, so you could be part of the play, but not be responsible if anything goes wrong!

D Behind the scenes. You like to make your mark in an understated way.

2 Your friends would describe you as...

A Confident and loud.

B Fearless and passionate.

C Excitable and crazy.

D Laid back and cool.

3 What bad habits of yours would annoy your band mates?

A You haven't got any bad habits!

B You can be a bit too serious sometimes.

C Your burping and parping!

D The random things you sometimes say.

5 If you do something wrong, how do you react?

A You never do anything wrong!

B Freak out a bit – you're a perfectionist!

C Shrug it off and try again until you get it right.

D It normally takes you too long to realise you've done anything wrong!

4 Two of your friends are fighting. How do you calm them down?

A You leave them to sort it out between themselves.

B You get them to talk about it.

C You distract them with some crazy dancing!

D What?! You hadn't even noticed!

TRIPP'S SUPER-GLUED TO ASH!

YOU TWO ARE INSEPERABLE!

Challenge

ARE YOU IN THE BAND?

Mostly As: Just like lead singer, Derek Jupiter, you are a natural front-man. Can you sing? Who cares if you can't! You've got the attitude, confidence and charisma to make an amazing lead singer! You don't listen to critics – in fact, the only person you really listen to is yourself!

Mostly Bs: You're hard-working, determined and totally talented – like Tripp! So you'd make a totally rockin' lead guitarist! If you can't play guitar, you'll put your heart and soul into learning. You believe in giving everything you do 110%!

Mostly Cs: Woo hoo, there's a party in town and it's called you! You really want to be part of the band, but you don't want the responsibility of being the singer or lead guitarist, so like Burger, you're suited to being the bass guitarist. You like the limelight sometimes, but not always.

Mostly Ds: The front of stage isn't for you, but you still want to be a big part of the band. So being a drummer like Ash would suit you down to the ground! The band would be nothing without you, but you get to do your own awesome thing towards the back of the stage!

---

6 Finish this sentence. Being the centre of attention is ...

A The best feeling ever!
B Cool, when it's for a particular reason.
C Great sometimes, but not all the time.
D Not for you – you like to let others take centre stage.

---

7 Someone's sold an embarrassing story about you to a newspaper! So you ...?

A Shrug it off. It's part of the territory when you're a world-famous rock star.
B Feel annoyed that they're focusing on that and not the band!
C You call that embarrassing? You have a ton of embarrassing stories about yourself!
D Well as long as your mum doesn't read it you don't mind ...

49

TOTALLY HILARIOUS!

Check out some of the funniest scenes from I'm In The Band!

RECORD BREAKERS: VEHICLES

Wow-ee! These vehicle-based record breakers are amazing!

2 Fastest flight around the world
Swiss pilot, Riccardo Mortara and his crew set this record in 2005. It took them 57 hours and 57 minutes. **Phew!**

1 Youngest driver to lead the racing World Championship
Lewis Hamilton won the 2008 Formula One season when he was only 23!

3 Most gold runs in a row in X Games history
BMX mega-star, Jamie Bestwick won gold for the fourth year running during X Games 16, 2010.

4 Highest jump on a mountain bike
Martyn Ashton is a mountain bike trails rider who holds this super-cool record.

5 Longest journey by powered paraglider
Canadian Benjamin Jordan flew 8008km west to east across Canada in 2009!

8 Most BMX wheelies in one minute
Guadalupe Alvarez did 167 BMX wheelies. **Incredible!**

6 Youngest pilot to fly an aeroplane and a helicopter
Jonathan Strickland broke this awe-inspiring record when he was just 14 years old!

7 World's fastest skateboarding dog
Tillman, the Californian bulldog, set the world record in 2009 by rolling 100 metres in 19.6 seconds!

9 World's heaviest bus pulled by hair
Letchemanah Ramasamy pulled a 7874 kg bus over 30 metres. **Eeek!**

10 Most BMX stoppies in one minute
This brill record goes to Travis Frohlich, who completed 115 stoppies on a BMX!

MONSTER

Find out about Monster Trucks with this awesome guide!

HOW DID IT START?

The first ever Monster Truck was invented in the early 80s by an American called Bob Chandler. He nicknamed his pick-up truck, BIGFOOT and added bigger axles, making his already impressive truck, even bigger and stronger. He then drove BIGFOOT over a pair of cars in a field to see how powerful the car was. Soon, more Monster Trucks were on the road, so the next step was to start racing in competitions!

THE FACTS!

How much do they weigh?
Monster Trucks weigh around a mind-boggling 5–6 tons each.

How big are their mega tyres?
66 inches tall by 43 inches wide.

How much do they cost to make?
Around £60,000! And that doesn't inc the engine, which can cost around £25 just by itself!

How many of them are there?
There are over 500 Monster Trucks in t world, but only around 100 of these are proper racing trucks.

TRUCKS RULE!

TRICKS OF THE TRADE

Monster Trucks can do all sorts of amazing tricks. Check out some of them here ...

Jumps
Jumps do what they say on the tin! They look super cool!

Wheelies
When the Monster Truck rides up on its two back wheels, it's called a wheelie!

Doughnuts
When the Monster Truck spins around and around it's called a doughnut — sooo ace!

What can you do in them?
What can't you do in them? There are tons of different tricks including jumps, doughnuts and wicked wheelies!

How fast can they go?
BIGFOOT has been driven at over 80 miles per hour, phew! Other Monster Trucks have been driven up to 65–70 miles per hour, but drivers usually only get up to 25–30 miles per hour.

DISNEY

Phineas and Ferb

MAD Inventions

Check out Phineas and Ferb's most awesome inventions!

THAT'S IT! I'M CALLING MOM!

THAT'S WHAT I'M TALKING ABOUT!

AQUATIC ACROBATICS

Imagine having your own underwater **theme park** in your back garden! Phineas and Ferb did!

TOTAL BLAST

This massive ride is shaped like a **ROBOT SHIP** but it doesn't need an expert, anyone can use it!

GIANT JELLY MONSTER

HOW SCARY... for Candace, but totally wicked – remember when the world's biggest jelly mold came to life and became a jelly monster?

SLIDE AWA

When the boys made the world's best water slide, Ferb **covered himself in butter** so that he could go down it faster!

HOLD ON TIGHT FOR THE RIDE OF YOUR LIVES!

HICCUP HORROR

When Isabella got really bad hiccups, Phineas and Ferb built a haunted house to scare them out of her!

IF THIS RIDE DOESN'T SCARE ME, YOUR HAIR WILL!

ROCKIN' ROLLERCOASTER

This fantastic theme park ride goes up, down, over and under the whole Tri-State Area where Phineas and Ferb live. **BEST. RIDE. EVER!**

WHO SAID FRUIT WAS FOR SOFTIES?!

FREAKY FRUIT

WOW! Phineas and Ferb created their own video game, but accidentally programmed themselves into it and met these fearsome fruit!

DOOFENSHMIRTZ GETS IN ON THE ACT

Not to be outdone, Dr. Doofenshmirtz has made some really mad-cap inventions. One of the craziest was the 'Turn-everything-evil-inator' which brought some giant jelly to life!

COOL 'N' CRAZY CAR

Take one family car and **stick rockets** on the back of it, like Phineas and Ferb did. Now you've got your very own **FLYING CAR!**

Think that Phineas and Ferb are complicated to draw? Think again!

DRAWING PHINEAS

1 Phineas has a triangular face that's slightly tilted. Draw it so that the top is completely straight, but the other two lines have a slight curve.

2 Next, draw a small line for his mouth and two oval shapes for his eyes – with one slightly behind the other.

3 Phineas' hair is made up of six spiky strands. We've numbered them to make it easier! Make sure that the strand of hair marked 2 is the longest. Now draw a number 3 in his left ear.

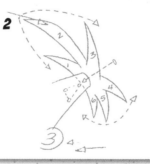

4 Phineas' eyes are usually flat against his head, but if you draw them upright, he looks completely different. You can also draw his open mouth, a half oval shape with two sets of little rectangles for his teeth.

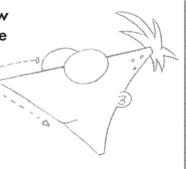

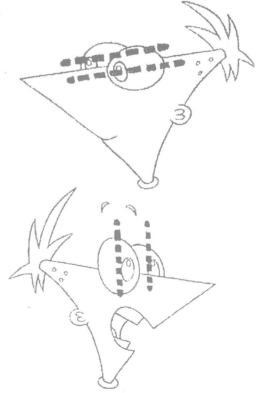

DRAWING FERB

1 Draw Ferb's head first – it's easy to do as it's shaped just like a baseball bat! Next, draw his nose. It's half a square, about half the way down his face. Now draw his mouth, which is just a tiny triangle. Finally, draw his ear, a little half circle.

2 Now on to Ferb's eyes. One eye is slightly smaller than the other. (Whether he's facing left or right, the bigger eye is further away.)

3 Ferb has eight sections of hair – as with Phineas, we've numbered the sections to make it easier to draw them!

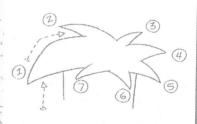

4 Draw the little reversed 3 in Ferb's ear and draw two dots for the pupils of his eyes.

Writer: Scott Peterson Pencils: John Green Inks: Mike DeCarlo Colors: Garry Black Letters: Michael Stewart Based on the series created by Dan Povenmire & Jeff "Swampy" Marsh

BEEP! BEEP! BEEP!

GREAT WORK, AGENT P.

MISSION ACCOMPLISHED.

UH, CAN I MAKE A SUGGESTION?

MAYBE WE SHOULD PUT DOOFENSHMIRTZ, I DON'T KNOW, IN JAIL THIS TIME?

CARL!

YOU KNOW, INSTEAD OF JUST LEAVING HIM CURSING ON THE FLOOR LIKE WE USUALLY DO.

JUST A THOUGHT.

EXCUSE ME, DON'T MEAN TO EAVESDROP, BUT... DO I HAVE A SAY IN THIS?

CURSE YOU AGAIN, PERRY THE PLATYPUS!

MEANWHILE...

HI, GUYS. WATCHA DOIN'?

WE'RE GONNA BREAK THE WORLD LAND SPEED RECORD!

...AND THEN MAYBE A SNACK.

BREAK THE RECORD, HUH?

COOL, I LIKE BREAKIN' THINGS.

THEN CLIMB ABOARD!

MOM! MOM! MOM! MOM! MOM!

YOU HAVE TO SEE WHAT THE BOYS ARE UP TO.

ACTUALLY, WHAT I HAVE TO DO IS GET TO MY HIGH-INTENSITY ORIGAMI CLASS.

SEE YOU LATER.

MOM IS NEVER HERE WHEN THE BOYS NEED BUSTING.

SOMETIMES I WISH I COULD JUST DO THE BUSTING MYSE--

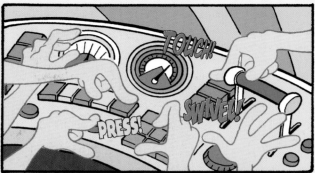

Disney Phineas and Ferb

Test your knowledge Mega Quiz

It's the ultimate Phineas and Ferb test! How much do you know about them?

1 What do the names of Dr. Doofenshmirtz's inventions usually end in?

2 What's Phineas' surname?

3 What's Ferb's surname?

4 What's the name of the town they live in?

5 Which character is described as more of a man of action than words?

6 Who once drank a growth elixir in an attempt to get taller?

7 What did Phineas and Ferb once build a passenger plane out of?

8 What is Isabella's pet Chihuahua called?

9 Finish the quote. "The enemy of platypus is ..."

10 Who is Phineas and Ferb's biggest fan?

11 What was Phineas and Ferb's heroic alter-ego called?

12 What was Linda's pop star name?

13 Name one of the Fireside Girls, apart from Isabella.

14 What is the Organisation Without a Cool Acronym (O.W.C.A) also known as?

15 What did the ray gun that Dr. Doofenshmirtz created make people do?

SO HOW WELL DO YOU KNOW THEM?

1-5: Seriously dude, you need a refresher course!
In one ear and out the other! It's time to re-read the intro and comic strips!

6-10: Pretty good, but you could definitely do better.
How about re-watching a few episodes to get your score up?

11-15: Well done, you've got an awesome result!
You've got the knowledge on Phineas, Ferb and the rest of the gang.

ANSWERS

PAGE 14

SCRAMBLED!

"Just putting the finishing touches on my latest evil plan."

THE MISSING WORD
Gorilla

PAGE 15

ODD PHINEAS OUT

D

PAGE 15

JIGSAW JUMBLE

1 **3**

PAGE 17

WORDSEARCH

PAGE 28

GET YOUR SKATES ON!

PAGE 29

TOTAL CHANGES

WHO IS IT?
Ginger

PAGE 32

SUPER SUDOKU

SKATER PILE UP

 = 5   = 6

PICTURE PUZZLER
The middle close-up

PAGE 35

KICK'S CATCHPHRASE
Showtime

PAGE 37

WORD SEARCH

SPOT THE DIFFERENCE

PAGE 46

PAGE 47

SHADOW ROCKER! **ASH TAYLO**
WORD PLAY BURGER PITT

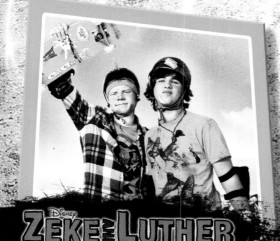